RADIO ANTENNAS

Michael Toia

JOKALYM PUBLISHING   **16206 Glenhollow Ct**   **Culpeper, VA 22701**
k3mt@arrl.net

SECOND EDITION

JANUARY 2017

Copyright © 2005, 2016 by Michael J. Toia

ISBN 978-0-9600859-2-7

PREFACE

Radio, and its antennas, have fascinated me from childhood. I would visit an uncle's home where there stood a beautiful, floor-model, broadcast receiver with shortwave bands. Uncle, an Italian immigrant, would listen to broadcasts from the Vatican and other countries. The languages were unintelligible to me. But father explained how signals from "the Old World" would travel all the way to us, in the Eastern U.S. That was it! I had to know how!

Father introduced me to radio receivers by way of a project. We built a one-tube, regenerative receiver, first for the broadcast band, then with plug-in coils for the shortwave bands. I would while away many an evening with my little wooden box, coil sticking out the top, and a Millen dial on its front, listening to - lo and behold - *radio hams* on the 75 meter band. This just threw gasoline on my burning desire to learn. Father then explained what ham radio was, and brought me a few magazines about it, complete with how to learn the Morse code.

About that time I met a wonderful chap. He had just been discharged from the Navy, had been a radio operator aboard a destroyer, and now was stringing a dipole for 40 meters between two houses. By stroke of luck, I lived across the street. My new mentor, W3SJK (now a *silent key*) [1] took me under his wing, taught me Morse, and got me through licensing as a novice amateur radio operator. In amateur radio parlance, he was my "Elmer." [2]

From that time on, I have been installing, designing, using, and studying antennas. This publication leads you, the reader, through my virtual antenna farm, where I share my concepts and understanding of the antenna. I limit my scope to those I love so, the wire antennas, most often used below 500 MHz. But the same principles apply to two- and three-dimensional antenna structures, such as bow-ties, biconicals, corner- and parabolic-reflectors, for all such structures can be modeled as a mesh of one-dimensional wires

---

[1] A deceased radio amateur

[2] One who mentors another in obtaining an amateur radio license, from a nostalgic story years back told by an amateur so mentored.

Author's notes

This work began as an invited lecture, first at the engineering corporation where I worked, and then before a local meeting of the IEEE Antenna and Propagation Society. My goal here is the addition of explanatory text to those lecture notes, resulting in a product that stands alone, with no need for me to stand up and explain a group of slides.

The antennas I discuss are all simple structures made of wire. Many very useful designs are made of nothing more that wires or other thin, linear metal members such as rods or tubes. Examples are vee beams, rhombics, longwires, which I do not discuss, and the dipole, ground plane, yagi, quad, and log periodics, which I do.

The principles I explain should enable the studied reader to tackle analysis of just about any antenna, particularly those made of thin, linear metal elements. To do the complicated math, the reader should invest in some form of "Method of Moments" computer software for PCs, such as one of the NEC products. Advertisements for "Numerical Electromagnetic Code" appear in several journals, and on the internet. Lately a free program, 4NEC2, is available for download on the internet. Obtain a product that can handle at least 150 segments.

Dedication

To my Elmer, Earl Fowkes, W3SJK. I remain forever grateful that you took the time to introduce a young boy to the wonderful world of ham radio, and therethrough, to a fascinating career field.

INDEX

DEFINITION

What is a Radio Antenna?

Your interest in this book shows that you have a concept of the antenna. But to be precise, we should define it. There are a few ways to do that. An antenna is:

- an interface between a transmitter (or receiver) and radio waves.
- a type of *transducer*. As a loudspeaker converts electrical current into audible sound, an antenna converts current - electrons vibrating on a wire - to photons - the particles of electromagnetic radiation.
- a carefully crafted metal assembly designed to produce, or receive, radio waves.

These are all proper definitions. There are others. But, in my studies and efforts, I have adopted a rather glib, yet straightforward, definition:

- An antenna is a bent piece of wire.

As you review the material to follow, you may come to embrace this definition.

A colleague recently commented on my lecture, saying "All antennas have already been invented." I was taken aback by this. My rebuttal is simple. If an antenna is a bent piece of wire, then all possible antennas consist of all possible wire lengths, each bent in one of many infinite sets of all possible angles, with an infinite number of bends. Thus, give me an antenna of your choice, and I can bend it at its middle, thus forming another antenna that may have different properties, sometimes useful as well.

Antenna Engineering

The art of antenna engineering becomes the simple art of deciding how much wire to use, where to bend it, how many bends to make, which way to make each bend, and how far. The art requires that we find the current flowing on every tiny part of the wire. The latter problem is today solved by use of computer code (i.e, a computer program). Numerical Electromagnetic Code (NEC) is one such program suite. The results calculated to produce exhibits later in this work were done with NEC-4, available from Roy Lewallen, W7EL, listed on the internet.

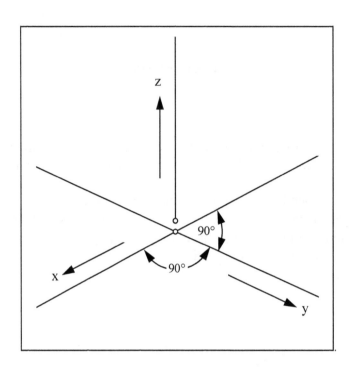

GROUND PLANE ANTENNA
FIGURE 2-1

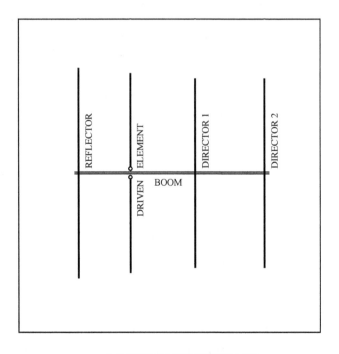

A FOUR ELEMENT YAGI
FIGURE 2-2

2

SOME COMMON ANTENNAS

The Ground Plane

This simple antenna, Figure 2-1, can be made of four individual wires, each bent at a right angle at its middle. By fusing halves of four wires into one in the vertical direction (the z-axis), the other halves can be turned to run along four horizontal directions, namely, the x-axis and y-axis. Power is applied or removed by cutting the z-axis wire at the origin and providing a small gap, where transmission line can be attached, as shown in the figure.

The Yagi

Yagi antennas are a sequence of parallel, nearly half-wave dipoles. A dipole at one end is about 5% longer than the classical half-wavelength. The next one is a bit shorter than a half-wavelength, and the remaining are all about 5% shorter than the second. The dipoles are spaced approximately 0.2 wavelength apart. These dimensions are approximate. Various designs use different dipole lengths and inter-dipole spacing.

The first dipole is called the reflector. The second is cut at its center, where feed line is attached, and is called the driven element. The third and succeeding dipoles are called directors. All dipoles are mounted on a mechanical support called the boom, which runs at right angles to the elements and supports them at their centers. The boom is usually metal, but due to symmetry, carries no current. It can be any conducting or insulating material. Figure 2-2 is the layout of a yagi. It is a planar structure: all elements and boom are located on one plane.

The reflector, because of its proximity to the driven element, is excited (has current forced to flow on it) by both electrical and magnetic induction from the driven dipole. Since it is spaced a bit from the driven element, its excitation is retarded a bit in phase. Further, by making it a bit too long, more phase shift takes place. Its current flow radiates radio waves that are out of phase with the driven element in the direction to the rear of the boom, but on reaching the driven element in the forward direction, are more nearly in phase.

Thus the two act in concert to increase the radio signal in the forward direction, down the boom to the right in the figure, and to cancel radiation in the rearward direction (to the left). See Chapter 9 for more detail.

The directors are similarly excited. But their shorter length makes their currents advanced in phase, countering the delay caused by spacing, so they add to the radio wave reflected down the boom in the forward direction. The radio wave in the forward direction is reinforced by the directors. More may be added to further increase the radiated field strength in this direction. But additional reflectors are practically useless, because the first one cancels the radio wave traveling in the reverse direction, and there is thus very little radio energy to excite the 2nd or more reflectors.

The yagi is perhaps misnamed. It is the invention of Dr. Uda, and his associate, Dr. Yagi. The latter translated their work to English. Thank you, Dr. Yagi, for allowing me to understand Uda's work. These antennas are more correctly known as Yagi-Uda arrays. [3]

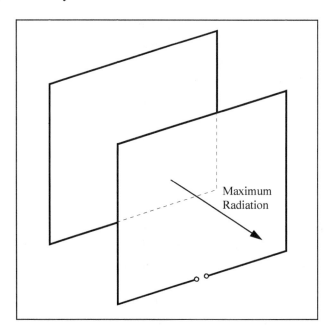

THE CUBICAL QUAD
FIGURE 2-3

The Quad Loop and the Cubical Quad

---

[3] A sidenote: my friend and colleague, Ron Payne, related this story which I had not previously heard. Yagi toured the US and other places, describing this antenna, and hardly mentioned Uda. This supposedly led to the demise of their friendship.

I first met the cubical quad at age 14. It fascinated me then, and continues to do so. An example of the "bent wire" definition, it is a pair of planar, square (four sided - hence "quad") loop antennas sharing a common normal, separated by about 0.2 wavelengths. See Figure 2-3. Each loop is thus one wavelength in circumference.

While the square shape has most often been used, other shapes work as well. In particular, the circular and triangular shapes have appeared in the literature, the latter known as the "delta loop" beam. Two square loops have eight corners. These define the corners of a cube if the loops were spaced a quarter wave apart. Thus the name "cubical" quad.

In a later chapter I show how to estimate the current flow on a long wire. One can conceive of the quad loop as a full-wavelength wire, cut at the center, with the two ends folded back and connected together. It mimics a design known as "two half waves in phase." Borrowing now from the later chapter, note that the current at the ends *should* be zero, when the electrons have nowhere to go. But here the electrons *do* have a place to go. As a result, the current at the feed point is a maximum, so the input impedance has its lowest value, about 130 ohms.

Notice that a folded dipole pulled apart to a square shape produces the loop.

The Spiral Loop Antenna

At low frequencies, with wavelengths much greater than a few meters, input impedance of "small" antennas [4] is quite low, and difficult to handle. In an attempt to increase the impedance, some are wound as a many-turn loop. This loop, Figure 2-4, is a fine example of a "bent wire" application, used for direction finding. It has had a long history as an effective, yet small, direction-finding loop, dating from WW I to modern times. The one shown here has five turns and is wound on a cross made of two 1 x 3 wood planks.

Spiral loops wound on a piece of stiff cardboard were used in broadcast radio receivers before ferrite rod antennas were developed. They were often found in the rear of pre-WW II home-entertainment radios.

---

[4] An antenna is "small" when its maximum dimension is a fifth of a wavelength or less.

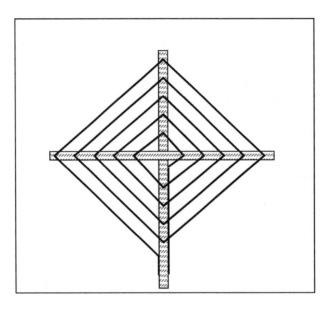

SQUARE SPIRAL LOOP ANTENNA
FIGURE 2-4

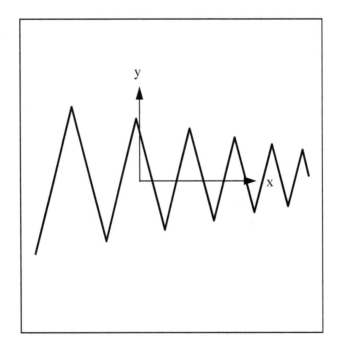

ZIG-ZAG LOG PERIODIC STRUCTURE
FIGURE 2-5

Zig-Zag Logarithmically Periodic Structure

The basic zig-zag wire, Figure 2-5, is my last entry into the "bent wire" definition. This particular structure starts by stretching a wire perpendicular to a line (the x axis) for two inches, and parallel to the line for minus one inch (a 2:1 ratio), then returning the wire back to the line, but another inch in the negative x direction.. Then stretch wire to the other side of the line 10% more, to 2.2 inches perpendicular and 1.1" parallel to the line, and returning again another 1.1" further along the line. This motif is continued until the builder runs out of wire, patience, or need.

Interestingly, these antenna structures repeat their pattern and impedance every time the frequency changes from one value to a fractional ratio above that value - 90%, in this example. If the smallest zig-zag is $1/20^{th}$ of the last, largest one, the antenna will work over a frequency range of abut 20:1. The pattern and impedance, changing in this *geometric* progression, repeats with the logarithm of the frequency - hence the *log periodic* name.

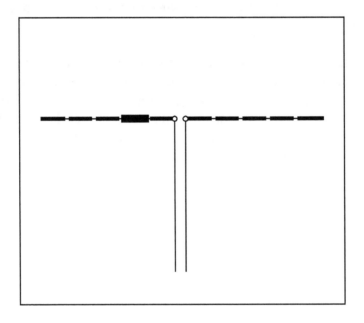

HALF-WAVE DIPOLE IN TEN SEGMENTS
FIGURE 3-1

8

3

SEGMENTS

A wire antenna is a sequence of very short wire segments connected together, end-to-end. Two-dimensional antennas, such as patches and reflectors, can be made of "chicken wire" structures of connected wire segments. I can look at a half wave dipole as a string of ten (or any number) of segments all connected, end to end, as in Figure 3-1, where I've emphasized one of the segments for further study.

The segments are sized to follow these general rules:

- No segment is more than $1/20^{th}$ wavelength long, or so.
- Segments are all thin, with a ratio of length to diameter of 10:1 or so.

By "or so" I mean these rules are not hard and fast. Violating them a bit causes some inaccuracies in calculating the overall pattern and impedance.

The fundamental basis of the segment approach is found in theory books on electromagnetics (radio waves). The defining equation [5] just says the following. The electric field is proportional to the magnetic field. The latter is proportional to a *Vector Potential* field, the *A* field. In turn, the *A* field, a vector:

- is proportional to the current flowing on the segment.
- is proportional to the length of the segment.
- falls off as distance increases (inverse distance, or 1/d, variation).
- is delayed in phase as distance increases.
- is parallel to the segment.

The length of the segment, times its current, is called a **current moment**, an important concept in calculating the radio field set up by the segment.

The field oscillates in time. To study antennas, we freeze time at one particular instant, when the current in a reference segment is at its maximum and pointing in a chosen direction.

---

[5] See, for example, Eqn. 9.3, p 269, Jackson, "Classical Electrodynamics," J. Wiley & Sons, Fifth Printing, August, 1966 - the equation that first showed me that, indeed, "The current *does* do the talking."

Far Field Condition

Very far from an antenna, the electric field is proportional to the *A* field. Since *A* is always parallel to the current moment, it can be leaning toward or away from the line of sight. Only the part perpendicular to the line of sight generates an electric field. Figure 3-2 shows the general case of a segment oblique to the line of sight. If we photograph the segment's **current moment** with a common security camera, as shown, we can "see" the direction and strength of the electric field.

Clearly, as distance doubles, the field appears half as strong. This is the linear 1/d dependence: doubling distance causes the electric field to drop to half strength, and power to drop one quarter strength - a 6 dB decrease. [6] Also note that the part of the moment leaning toward the camera contributes nothing to the *E* field.

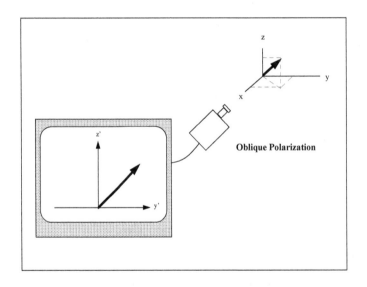

ELECTRIC FIELD AT A DISTANCE FROM A SEGMENT`
FIGURE 3-2

---

[6] For the more advanced reader: this is the source of the "-20 log(d)" term in free-space propagation calculations.

The Far Field

Far field conditions require the following items to be true.

- The security camera must be beyond "induction field" limits. This is generally guaranteed at distances beyond 20 wavelengths.
- Lines from all segments must be essentially parallel at the camera position. That is, the camera must see the antenna as a "point source."

Polarization

The E field has a direction, called its polarization. Figure 3-2 shows an oblique, linear polarization. It is neither vertical nor horizontal *seen at the monitor camera position*. **If the segment is seen end-on, as in Figure 3-3, there is *no E* field!** That is, **segments do not radiate off their ends**.

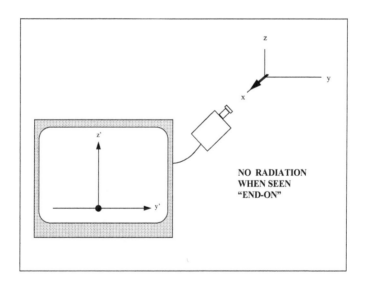

NO RADIATION FROM A SEGMENT'S END
FIGURE 3-3

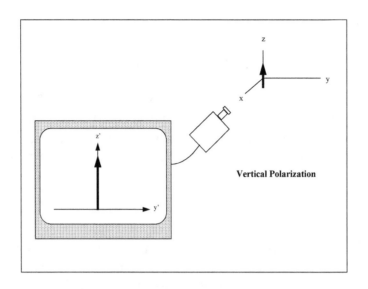

**VERTICAL POLARIZATION
FROM A VERTICAL CURRENT MOMENT
FIGURE 3-4**

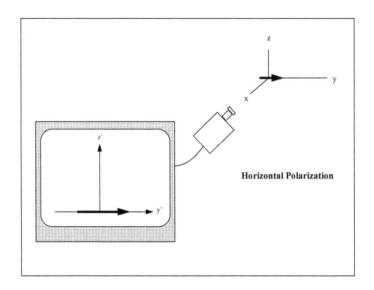

**HORIZONTAL POLARIZATION
FROM A HORIZONTAL CURRENT MOMENT
FIGURE 3-5**

If the segment is vertical, as in Figure 3-4, we say the field is vertically polarized. If it is horizontal, as in Figure 3-5, the field is horizontally polarized.

To calculate the *E* field of a single segment in the far field, do the following.

1. Draw the segment's current moment.
2. The moment's vector is parallel to the segment.
3. The length of the vector is the magnitude of current, times the length of the segment.
4. View the moment with a common security camera.
5. Look at the camera monitor, and trace the moment on its screen.
6. The direction of the trace is the *E* field polarization.
7. The length of the trace is proportional to field strength.
8. The *E* field is in the plane of the screen.
9. The field is proportional to the sine of the angle between the moment vector and direction to the camera.
10. The trace is inversely proportional to distance from the segment.

These principles are key to understanding how antennas produce their radiation patterns and the polarization of radio fields. The next chapter relies heavily on the developments just given, which are the fundamental teachings of this book. I recommend you bookmark this chapter and refer back to it as you proceed through the remaining chapters, and through other books or articles on antennas.

NOTES

SINGLE SEGMENT RADIATION PATTERN

What is a Radiation Pattern?

A pattern shows how much signal leaves a radio antenna in each direction. To measure or calculate one, put the antenna at the center of a large glass globe. From any point on the globe the antenna should look like a tiny glob.

Draw latitude and longitude lines on the globe at 5° intervals. [7] Connect a transmitter to the antenna, and walk about the globe. At each latitude/longitude intersection, measure the radio field strength, in dB relative to one microvolt per meter - that is, in dBuV/m. [8] With a permanent marker, write the value on the globe at that point. Do the same at every latitude/longitude intersection.

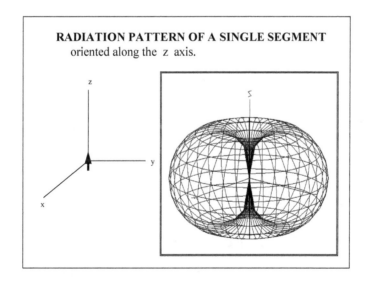

RADIATION PATTERN OF A SINGLE SEGMENT
oriented along the z axis.

3-D PATTERN
FIGURE 4-1

---

[7] Or other choice of "granularity."

[8] This is a standard measure of electric field strength. Calculate it as follows. Convert each reading to microvolts per meter. Then take its logarithm, and multiply by 20. Fore example, 2 uV/m = +6.02 dBuV/m.

Find the maximum reading. Label this point "zero." Go to every point. Subtract its reading from the maximum. Every new number will be less than or equal to the first, which will be zero. Write these new numbers at every point, after erasing the old number.

Connect a very stiff, transparent fiber from the center of the globe to each of the points. Divide the fibers into fifty equal-length parts. Then shorten each fiber by cutting off the value written on the globe. For example, the maximum value is 0 dB, so this fiber will be 50 units long. At the -6 dB point, the fiber will be 44 units long. At -10 dB, 40 units, at -20 dB, thirty units, and so forth. For any value less than -50 dB, just remove that fiber. [9]

Now connect a black thread from every fiber to its four nearest fibers. This will make the three - dimensional antenna pattern. In this way, the pattern of a single vertical segment, shown in Figure 4-1, was generated.

Notice that along the z axis, the signal strength is very weak - in fact, it drops to nothing at all. This is because segments do not radiate off their ends. But along the equator, the radiation is a maximum, 0 dB. Segments seen "broadside" appear at maximum length on a viewing security camera, so the E field is maximum in these directions. Looking at the segment from any other latitude/longitude produces an E field less than 0 dB, relative to the maximum. field value.

Isotropic Antenna

You'll hear of this antenna. It's a reference where all dB values around the globe are zero. It cannot be actually constructed. Its pattern is totally spherical.

Azimuth and Elevation Patterns

3-D patterns are nice to look at, but sometimes difficult to interpret. So we take "cuts" through them, like slicing an apple in two, to get a better idea of what is happening. A slice through the equator, in the x-y plane, produces an **azimuth** pattern, and a slice through the north and south poles produces an **elevation** pattern.

---

[9] This system uses a scale of -50 to 0 dB. Other scales can also be used, and are.

15

Figure 4-2 shows azimuth and elevation pattern cuts of Figure 4-1.

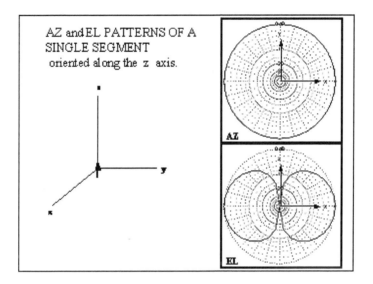

AZIMUTH AND ELEVATION PATTERN
FIGURE 4-2

Azimuth and Elevation patterns have a scale in dB, relative to the zero dB maximum value: these are called relative power patterns. The dB scale runs, from the outer circle inward, at values of 0, -2, -4, -6, -8, -10, -12.5, -15, -17.5, -20, -25, -30, -35, -40, -45, dB, and the central point is -50 dB.

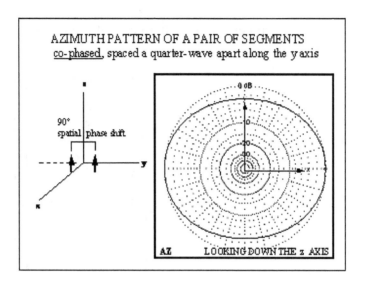

AZIMUTH PATTERN
PAIR OF SEGMENTS
FIGURE 5-1

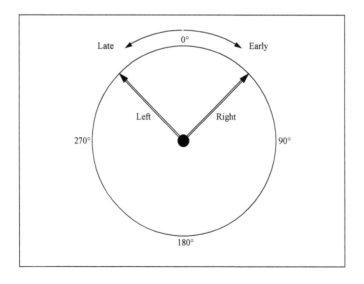

PHASOR DIAGRAM
FIGURE 5-2

17

5

TWO-SEGMENT RADIATION PATTERNS

Antennas consist of multiple segments. To understand how these produce an overall pattern, study first how two segments interact. This chapter looks at typical two-segment separations.

Quarter Wave Spacing

Figure 5-1 shows the azimuth pattern of a pair of segments spaced a quarter wavelength apart. Both are oriented vertically, are on the y axis, and penetrate the x-y plane. They are driven with equal currents, in time (temporal) phase. Viewed from a distance along the x axis, the *E* fields from both are vertical. Since the two segments are the same distance from the camera, their pattern has a relative maximum - 0 dB - in this direction, and along the negative x axis.

But seen from along the positive y axis, something happens. The two segments are *not* the same distance from the camera. They have a *spatial* phase shift of 90° in this direction. The *E* field is again vertically polarized, but the segment on the left in Figure 5-1 is farther from the camera than the one on the right. So the radiation from the two does not arrive in phase! The spatial phase separation causes a temporal phase shift in the y-direction. We account for the phase shifts by use of *phasors*.

Phasor Diagrams

Figure 5-2 is a *phasor* diagram. It shows the relative timing of two or more signals: here our signals are the *E* field strength. Phasor diagrams do **not** say anything about the *E* field direction, only its amplitude and timing. I'll discuss amplitude later, only timing here.

In a phasor diagram, a timing reference point is chosen anywhere the designer wants, often at the center of the antenna.

I've done that here. The arrow on the right of Figure 5-2's diagram shows that, along the positive y axis, radiation from the right segment reaches the camera early, by one-eighth of a cycle, or 45°. The left segment's radiation arrives late by the same amount. To get the total **E** field strength, I add the two phasors by putting the tail of one on the head of the other, as shown.

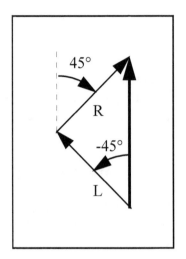

The sum of delayed and advanced fields is the hypotenuse of the right triangle so formed, or 1.4 times the field of one sector acting alone   Furthermore, the temporal phase of the total field is at reference phase, neither early nor late. The center of the antenna is often the best phase reference location, especially when there are far more than two segments.

The point to be made becomes more clear if I take the position of the left-hand segment to be the phase reference point. Then, along the positive y axis, the right segment is 90° closer to the camera than the left, so the spatial separation generates the time phase shift depicted by this drawing. The effect is the same as above, but the phase shift in this view is equal to the spacing between segments.

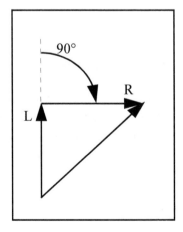

19

Seen along the negative y-axis, the right phasor is late compared to the left. The phasor diagram for this camera position (negative y axis) is the previous diagram, flipped 180° around a vertical line through its center. Although the early/late situation for the right segment has reversed, the total field has not changed in amplitude. Its phase, however, referenced to the left segment is now 45° late, whereas it had been 45° early.

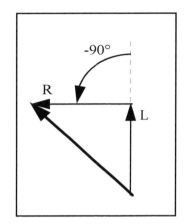

In general, then, as the two segments are spaced farther apart, the right phasor rotates more and more about a pivot point through its tail, at the head of the left segment phasor. Along the x axis, the phasor rotations are zero degrees: both are the same distance from the camera. The two phasors thus point straight up. The field strength is twice the field of one sector, as indicated in this phasor diagram.

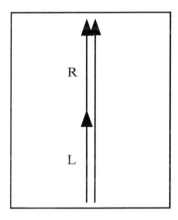

So, along the y axis, the previous two phasor diagrams shows the field to be 1.4/2.0 times the maximum field of 2.0, or 0.7 times the maximum field. This is a drop of 3 dB (work it out on a calculator: dB = 20 x log(0.7)). The pattern, Figure 5.1, shows this drop along the positive or negative y axis.

As the alignment of the two phasors with the segments equidistant from the camera occurs along the positive and negative x axis, the *E* field In this direction is twice the amplitude of the field for one phasor alone, and has increased by 6 dB. This situation is that of maximum field strength, for at any other azimuth angle, the right segment's phasor is no longer parallel to the left segment's phasor.

Half Wave Spacing

Next, the two segments are separated a half wavelength along the y axis. The field strength along the x axis is unchanged, because both segments are still the same distance from the cam era. The field still has its maximum value, the reference level, 0 dB, in this direction. But along the y-axis, the two phasors are 180 degrees apart, and cancel. This produces a null in that direction: see Figure 5-3. There is also a null along the positive and negative z axis, because segments do not radiate off their ends.

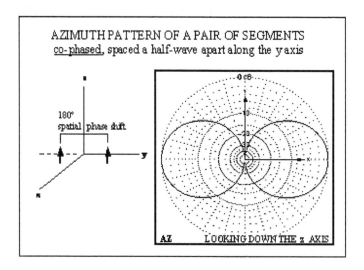

FIGURE 5-3

The phasor diagram at the right shows the phasors just shy of total cancellation, when the intra-segment spatial separation is 170° Total cancellation occurs when the 170° angle reaches 180°. Figure 5-3 is the resulting radiation pattern. So the general concept of using phasors to convert the sector's spatial phase displacements to temporal phase shift at the camera position, is really rather simple. In complex antennas, there are more than two segments, so there are more phasors, one per segment.

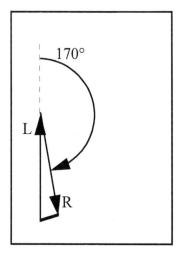

21

The *length* of each phasor is equal to the magnitude of a segment's current moment, and its rotation is equal to the difference in spacing, measured in degrees of one radio wave cycle, between the reference point and the segment. Again, phasors do not indicate *direction* of the electric field, only its relative time phase and amplitude.

If 90° separation brings about a 3 dB drop along the y axis, and 180° separation causes cancellation, is there a separation that causes the *E* field to have exactly *half* its maximum value? Here's the answer: make a phasor diagram where the sum of two phasors is equal in length to either phasor. An equilateral triangle results. In this case, the right phasor is rotated 120° *early*, compared to the left phasor. Rotation 120° late does the same thing, and the diagram is just flipped, right-to-left.

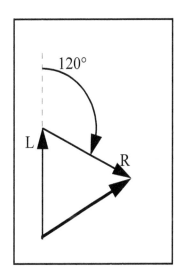

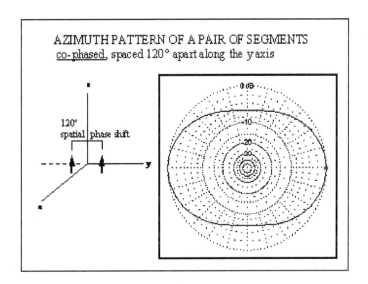

FIGURE 5-4

When NEC software calculates the pattern for the 120° segment separation, Figure 5-4 is the result. As predicted, the pattern has its maximum along the x axis. Along the positive and negative y axis, the field is just one-half as strong, or 6 dB below maximum.

Examine the case when the two segments are separated still more, to 270°. The phasor diagram along the positive y axis shows the right phasor to be early by 270°. As usual, the total field strength is the hypotenuse of a right triangle, so is 1.414 times the field of a single segment, or 0.707 times the field along the x axis. Figure 5-5 shows the pattern for this separation.

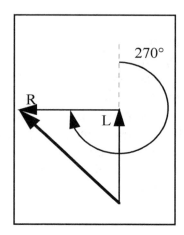

With the inter-segment separation more than 180°, there's some line between the x and y axis where one segment will be exactly 180° farther from the camera than the other. In every such direction the pattern will have a null, because the two segments are in time phase but spatially are exactly out of phase. Figure 5-5 shows such nulls, and resulting *sidelobes*.

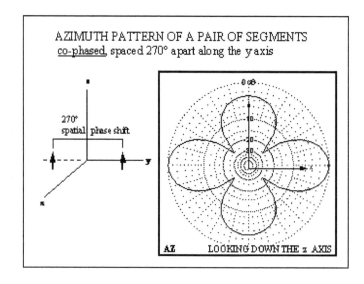

FIGURE 5-5

When the segments separate still farther, to 360°. the right phasor is again aligned with the left, and there is equal E field strength along both x and y axes. However, the nulls and sidelobes persist, and are moved about a bit, as is clear from Figure 5-6.

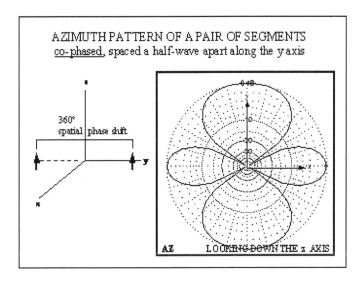

AZIMUTH PATTERN OF A PAIR OF SEGMENTS
co-phased, spaced a half-wave apart along the y axis

FIGURE 5-6

In many applications, two segments can be excited out of phase in time. Common examples are phase reversal, where one segment's current is flowing "up" while another's is flowing "down."   When two segments are spaced apart along the y axis, but one is driven in time exactly 180° out of phase with the other, the phasors *viewed along the x axis* cancel: there's a null on this direction. The phasor diagram to the right shows this situation, as does Figure 5-7 below.

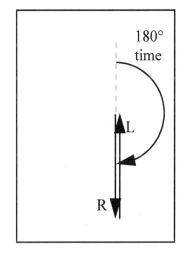

But viewed along the y axis, the right phasor rotates still further clockwise - in the early direction - so the pattern does not stay at a null until the right phasor rotates through another 360°. or multiples of 360°. With the segments separated by 180°, the two will be in phase along the y axis. This happens to the pattern of Figure 5-7.

24

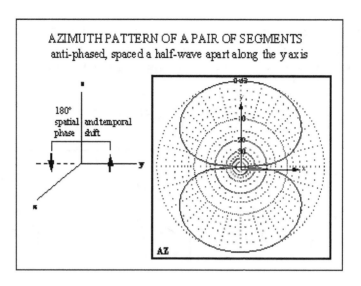

FIGURE 5-7

Cardioid Pattern

In Figure 5-8, the right segment current is 90° late, compared to the left. When viewed along the positive x axis, the two phases are 90° apart and the relative field is 1.4 times the value for an in-phase situation. But when viewed along the positive y axis, the 90° spacing difference causes the right phasor to be "early" by 90°, so the two are in phase: the pattern has a maximum. Along the *negative* y axis, the right phasor is 90° *later*, and cancels the left phasor, creating a null.

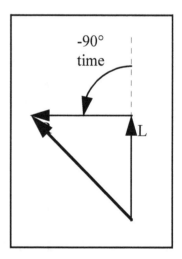

This cardioid (heart-shaped) pattern is often used in direction finding applications. It responds well to a signal except in a fairly narrow sector, where the signal becomes weak, and can disappear. Practical applications rotate an antenna about a mast between two vertical dipoles (each just a stack of segments similar to the pair discussed here) and note the orientation of the antenna when the signal disappears. The signal is arriving from that particular direction.

25

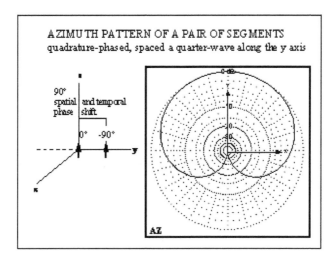

FIGURE 5-8

Finally, put two segments, one above the other, on the z axis. Their pattern is calculated just as has been done for two segments spaced along the y axis, with segments seen "end-on." The *E* field disappears in such a direction.

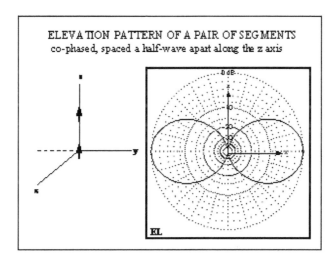

FIGURE 5-9

The curious reader can make up the phasor diagrams for these two cases. Just refer back to the phasor diagram for segments separated 180° along the y axis for the first, cophased, case, and rotate the phase of one segment by 180° for the second, antiphased, case. Two patterns result, one for cophased segments, the other for antiphased. These are shown in Figures 5-9 and 5-10.

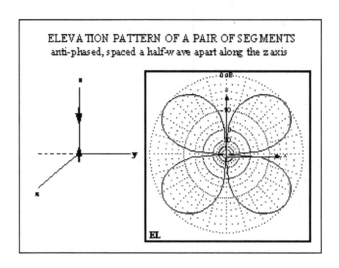

FIGURE 5-10

27

6

PATTERNS FROM THIN WIRES

Many antennas, such as dipoles, yagis, etc, are made of a thin wire or collection of thin wires. By understanding some basic properties of wire radiation patterns, you can "doodle out" many antenna patterns with just a scrap of paper, or even in thin air. This chapter discusses how to do that.

Properties of Wires

There are four basic properties of a wire that affect its radiation pattern. They are:

1. Current at the end of a wire must be zero. Electrons cannot leap off into the air.
2. Current every **odd** quarter wavelength from an end will have a maximum value.
3. Current every **even** quarter wavelength from an end will be at a minimum.
4. Current reverses direction at each minimum point.

These hold for a "natural" current distribution on wires, and are shown in Figure 6-1.

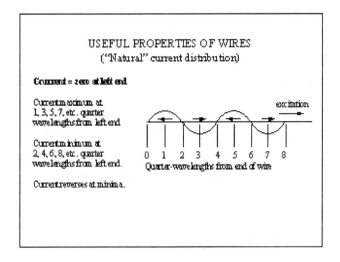

FIGURE 6-1

Using the Properties to "See" a Pattern

Let's look at a wire antenna and visualize its pattern. I present a clever bent wire, the "Half-Square" antenna of Figure 6-2.

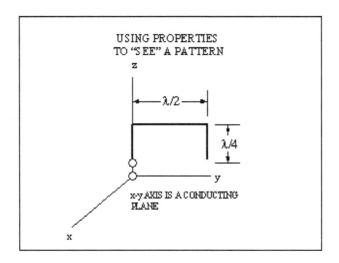

THE HALF-SQUARE ANTENNA
FIGURE 6-2

This antenna is a full wave (360° electrical degrees) wire. It rises one quarter wave from a large, conducting ground plane, then runs horizontally for a half wave, and finally dives back toward the ground plane for the final quarter wave of its length. The whole wire is elevated just a bit so neither bottom end contacts the ground plane. The antenna is driven between the bottom left end and the ground plane. Can you "see" its pattern? Of course you can: here's how. First, sketch out the current flow.

- Zero - bottom of right-hand vertical section, as this is the end of the wire.
- First maximum - quarter wave back toward feedline, top of right hand vertical section, and right end of horizontal section.
- First minimum - another quarter wave back, center of half-wave horizontal section.
- Current reversal - center of the horizontal section.
- Next maximum - another quarter wave back, left hand side of horizontal section, and top of left vertical section.
- Next minimum - bottom of left vertical section.

29

Figure 6-3 shows the current pattern on the antenna. Remember, we "freeze" the rapidly oscillating current at one instant in time, where the currents are momentarily flowing as shown.

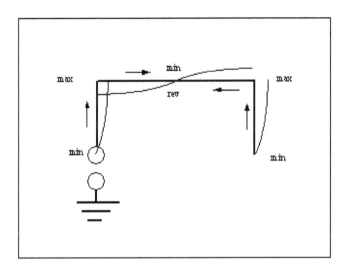

CURRENT PATTERN ON THE HALF-SQUARE
FIGURE 6-3

Now, what is this antenna's pattern?

<u>Along the x axis (directly out of or into the paper):</u>

- The horizontal part is a line of segments and current moments. For each (current) moment [18] on the right half, there is an identical moment on the left half. What one giveth, the other taketh away: segment by segment, the radiation cancels. **There is no field radiated by the top part!** So there is no horizontally polarized field.
- The right and left vertical parts are each a stack of segments/moments. For each segment on the right, there is a matching segment on the left. But along the x axis, these are equidistant from the camera position, so their E fields add. **The radiation along the x axis is maximum, and vertically polarized.**

---

[18] By this time you should be used to the term *moment* as a product of current and segment length.

<u>Along the y axis (horizontally, in the plane of the paper):</u>

- The horizontal part's segments are all seen end-on. None radiate in this direction. Again, **The top part produces no field.**
- The two vertical parts are in time phase. But they are spatially separated by 180°. So their fields cancel totally. **There is no radiation at all along the y axis!**

<u>Along the z axis(straight up, in the plane of the paper):</u>

- The horizontal part is seen just as it was along the x axis. **There is no radiation from the horizontal part.**
- Both vertical parts are seen end-on. **There is no radiation at all along the z axis.**

This almost sounds perverse. If the horizontal part does not radiate, what does it do? It connects the two vertical parts together. Although it does not radiate along any of the three axes, consider what happens when we put the camera on a line midway between the positive x and y axis, or z and y axis. Now the horizontal segments on the left half are farther away than those on the right half, and radiation results. So, some horizontal field does happen, just not along the three axes.

Another point to be taken from Figure 6-3 concerns the antenna input impedance - what the transmitter "sees" when trying to deliver power to this antenna. Since it is fed at a point where the current is minimum, the voltage must be at a maximum. Impedance is just the voltage divided by the current, so the impedance is a maximum. This is characteristic of "voltage fed" antennas. Standard 50 ohm coaxial cable is not a good choice to feed this antenna. An antenna tuner is required.

Now, let's see what NEC calculates for the half-square: see Figure 6-4.

Interesting. The results we guessed are fairly close. The azimuth (AZ) pattern does show a fairly deep null (18 dB) along the y axis, and maximum along the x axis. The elevation (EL) pattern shows a similar 18 dB null along the z axis. But why are these nulls not total?

31

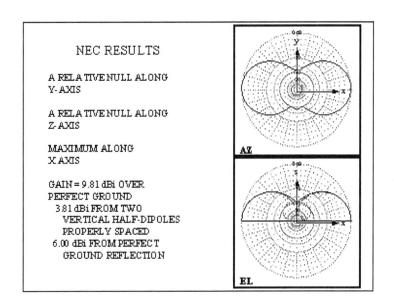

HALF-SQUARE ANTENNA
FIGURE 6-4

The answer is not immediately obvious, yet important. As the current travels from the feed point toward the end of the wire, it encounters wire resistance. First, the wire itself is resistive, so the current at the right half (horizontal and vertical parts) is not quite as strong as at the left half. But there is another reason for resistance. **The antenna radiates power!** This also attenuates the current as it travels down the wire. In fact, if this "radiation resistance" did not exist, neither would this book, nor radio itself.

Look more closely at the elevation pattern. Besides the solid outer line, there are two dotted lines, one heavier than the other. The heavier one is the vertically polarized *E* field, and the lighter, the horizontally polarized field. Viewing the antenna from the z axis shows that the vertical field vanishes. Both vertical parts of the antenna are seen end-on, and the horizontal part cannot produce vertical polarization because all of its segments are horizontal. But there is a small field, horizontally polarized, 18 dB below full power. This arises from the slight unbalance in currents between the two halves of the horizontal part.

This concludes a brief study of the properties of wires that have open ends. It applies to dipoles, log periodics, verticals, and many other common antennas.

7

RESONANCE AND IMPEDANCE

Current on a wire is due to the motion of electrons, parts of the atoms of which the wire is made. These charged particles flow on a wire at nearly the speed of light. Esoterically, no one electron moves that fast. But the motion is akin to a tube full of tennis balls. Push one ball into the left side, and all the balls move, with one falling out the right side.

Due to Murphy's law, Benjamin Franklin made a guess that current was the flow of positive charges in a wire. He guessed wrong. But for most electrical and electronic work, we assume current to be the flow of imaginary positive particles in a wire - that is, the reverse of electron flow.

Suppose I make a half-wave dipole antenna, a thin horizontal wire exactly one half wavelength, or 180°, long at a chosen operating frequency. I cut it at the center where I attach a voltage generator. At a time, t=0, I start a cycle of pulsing voltage across this gap. I produce a negative pulse, which starts pushing electrons toward the right.[19]

The electrons move toward the right, traveling at nearly the speed of light. They reach the end and pile up, where they repel one another. I pick my frequency so it takes one quarter of the generator's cycle to do this. Then they rebound, and in another quarter cycle they reach the middle, moving toward the left. At just this time the voltage turns around, assisting the electrons in their motion to the left. The generator has gone through a half-cycle at this time. Its voltage is exactly in phase with the current flow on the dipole.

In another quarter cycle, the electrons pile up at the left end of the dipole, and repel one another again. They begin flowing to the right, and in a final quarter cycle reach the middle, just in time for the generator to begin a new cycle. Figure 7-1 shows the sequence of voltage pulse and electron flow just described.

In this *resonant* condition, the voltage is exactly in step with the current, so a ratio of voltage to current has no phase shift.

---

[9] For the purist reader: any driving voltage, including the sine waves used in radio, can always be generated by a series of short pulses whose amplitude matches the voltage waveform at each time. See, for example, any text on Fourier Transforms, and/or Sampling Theory.

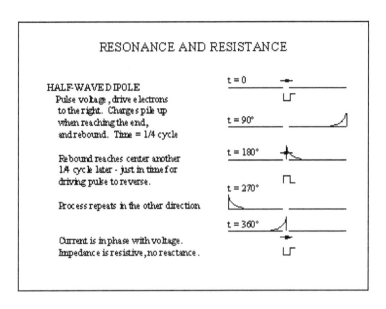

FIGURE 7-1

Half-wave dipoles, in fact, appear as a 76 ohm resistor to the generator.

Now watch what happens when the generator timing is slowed down, or speeded up, a bit. Figure 7-2 depicts this case. First, shorten the dipole a bit. The electrons reach the end in less than a quarter cycle. In my example, they take only 85° of the cycle to reach the end. They rebound, and reach the center in another 85° of driving cycle, or 170° overall, a bit early.

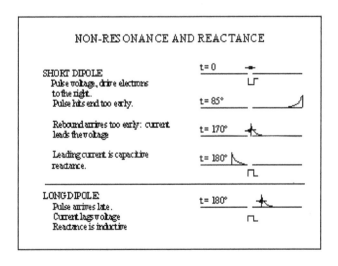

FIGURE 7-2

The current passes by the center, and the voltage reverses a bit later. This is a case of current *leading* the voltage. It is not exactly in phase with the driving cycle, and the effect is to have a resistance in series with a *capacitive* reactance.

If instead the antenna were lengthened a bit, the current would take longer to make the round trip, and would not quite reach the center when the voltage reverses. Then the voltage is ahead of the current, and the effect is to have a resistance in series with *inductive* reactance.

In general, the following are true:

- At their driving point, all antennas have some resistance.
- If the antenna is less than a quarter wavelength from drive point to end, it will behave as if it also has capacity in series with the resistance.
- If the antenna is a quarter wavelength from drive point to end, it will behave as if it were just a resistor. It is fed at a point of highest current, so its impedance will be low.
- If the antenna is longer than a quarter wavelength from drive point to end, it will behave as if it also has inductance in series with the resistance.
- When the antenna is two quarter waves from drive point to the end, it will again seem to be a resistance - but is voltage fed, so will have a high impedance.
- Antennas between a multiple of a half wave, and that plus a quarter wave long, will appear to be capacitive.
- Antennas between a multiple of a half wave, and that *minus* a quarter wave, will appear to be inductive.
- An antenna that is a multiple of a half wave long will be voltage fed, and have a high impedance.
- An antenna that is an *odd* multiple of a quarter wave long will be current fed, and have a low impedance.

These simple rules can often guide the designer in estimating the impedance of wire antennas.

- 8 -

PRACTICAL ANTENNAS - THE DIPOLE

Let's now look more closely at how antennas are analyzed, and how they work. First, take a simple center-fed dipole and cut it into five segments, as in Figure 8-1. The figure also shows the azimuth pattern calculated by NEC, and the fact that NEC calculated a 2.1 dBi gain for this antenna. But how did it arrive at this conclusion?

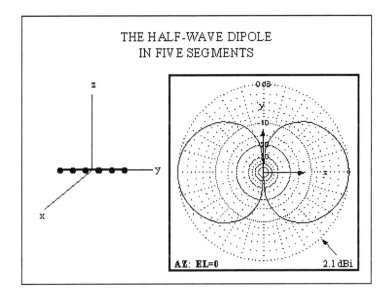

HALF WAVE DIPOLE IN FIVE SEGMENTS: NEC PATTERN
FIGURE 8-1

NEC calculates the current on all segments of the antenna. This could be done by hand, but the software solves some complicated equations and makes the job so much easier. Here is a list of the five segments, their currents, and their phases.

Segment	Amperes	Phase
1	0.36252	-6.13
2	0.83554	-3.31
3	1	0
4	0.83554	-3.31
5	0.36252	-6.13

TABLE 8-1

I told NEC to excite the antenna with one ampere on center segment 3, and this is the reference phase. NEC finds that the current on the segments toward either end fall off, and that the phase angle becomes slightly negative. From these data *you* can calculate the pattern. Although NEC does it faster, you should understand how.

Build the phasor diagrams. First, looking along the x axis in Figure 8-1, all segments are equal distances from the camera. So I see five phasors, all parallel to the x axis: the field in this direction is horizontally polarized. The phasor diagram starts this way.

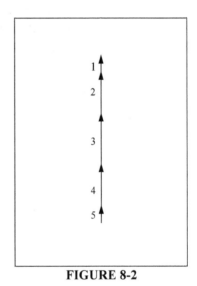

FIGURE 8-2

Notice, that the phasors **are not all equal in length**. Their lengths are proportional to the segments' moments. Although the *segments* are of equal length, they carry different currents. Thus the individual phasors have different lengths, proportional to their currents.

Another change occurs. The phasors of Figure 8-2 assume all currents to be in temporal phase. But the current table shows this not to be true. So each phasor must be adjusted in time phase to match the actual currents. This is shown in the phasor diagram to the right, Figure 8-3.

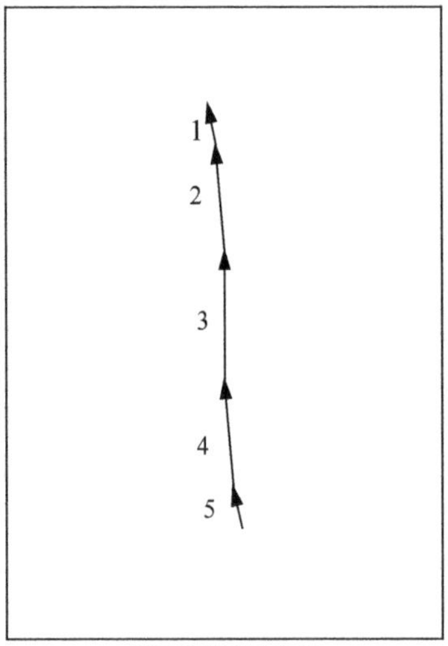

The effect of this temporal phase adjustment is twofold. First, the overall sum of phasors is a bit less than if all were in phase. Second, the overall phasor has a slight phase delay from the reference field set up by the center segment.

FIGURE 8-3

37

The discussion above shows how to calculate the field when looking along the x axis, or at any point in the x-z plane, where the view always sees the dipole "broadside." We already know that, looking at it from the y axis, all segments are seen end-on, so there is no field in this direction: the antenna pattern has a deep null. But what if we look at it, say, from any position that is some angle off the y axis, perhaps 60°? All these positions fall on a cone whose center is the y axis, and whose total included angle is 120°.

The centers of the five segments are spaced at different distances from the origin. What are these spacings? Figure 8-4 shows them. Segment spacings along the y axis are as follows: 1 = -72°   2 = -36°   3 = 0°   4 = +36°   5 = +72°.

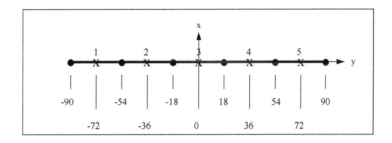

FIVE SEGMENT DIPOLE
SEGMENT SPACINGS FROM CENTER
FIGURE 8-4

If the dipole is viewed from the y axis, the segments are not all equidistant. Segment 5's center is 72° closer to the camera than segment 3, and segment 1 is 72° farther away than segment 3. Of course, there is no field in this direction, as all segments are being viewed end-on.

But I want to look at the dipole from a line making an angle of 60° off the y axis. Figure 8-5 shows the segments from this viewpoint. This bit of geometry uses the actual segment lengths and locations, **not the current moments!** Phasor diagrams, on the other hand, use current moments.

From Figure 8-5, notice that, at a 60° angle off the dipole axis, each segment's spacing from the camera is **half** the segment-to-segment spacing. This factor is the Cosine of the viewing angle. Therefore, to calculate the field *in this direction* the phasor diagram must be modified.

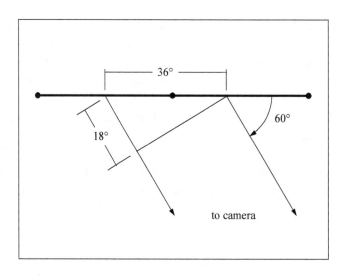

SPATIAL DELAY BETWEEN TWO ADJACENT SEGMENTS
FIGURE 8-5

Now mimic Figures 8-2 and 8-3. Segment 3 retains its reference phase, neither early nor late. Segment 4 is 36° from segment 3, so its phase is early by 18°, half of the spacing. Segment 2's phase is likewise late by this same amount. For identical reasons, segment 5's phase is early by 36°, and segment 1's phase, late by 36°. These spatial phase shifts must be added to the temporal shifts calculated by NEC to yield the total shift, as in the table below.

Segment	1	2	3	4	5
Temporal shift	-6.13°	-3.31°	0°	-3.31°	-6.31°
Spatial shift	-36.00°	-18.00°	0°	+18.00°	+36.00°
Total Shift	-42.13°	-21.31°	0°	+14.69°	+29.69°

The phasor diagram becomes modified as shown at the right.

There's one remaining detail to apply to this diagram. In Figure 8-5, the segments are not seen broadside, and thus the current moments are also seen at an angle. Hence, from point #9, page 13, the current moments must all be multiplied by the sine of 60°, or 0.866. The total field in this direction is then just slightly late, by a few degrees, from reference phase, and is 0.866 times the relative value shown.

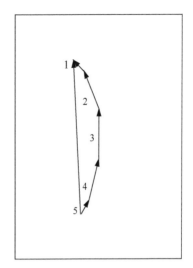

These details of phasor adjustment are time consuming, and prone to errors. That's why I defer to NEC software to take care of the gritty details. Not only does it calculate the interaction of one segment to all others and derive the currernts, it then does the phasor geometry and arithmetic, calculates the drive point impedance, and on demand generates the antenna pattern. Then, by adding up the relative power radiated at every direction of the pattern, generated by a unit power input which the user specifies, it "normalizes" the pattern by calculating the maximum gain, in dB over an isotropic antenna (dBi).

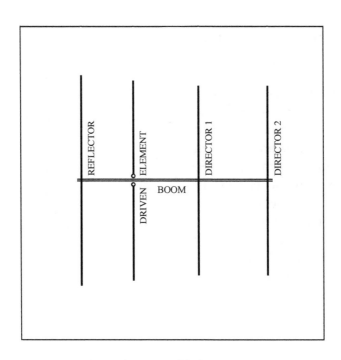

A FOUR ELEMENT YAGI
FIGURE 2-2

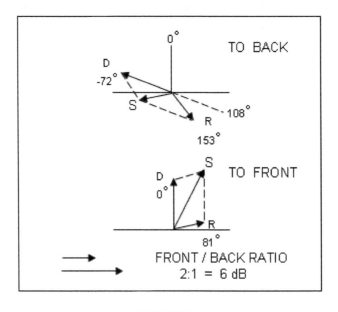

FIGURE 9-1

ANATOMY OF THE YAGI

Professors Hidetsugu Yagi and Shintaro Uda designed and constructed the first multi-dipole, parasitic antenna bearing their names: the Yagi-Uda array. It was 1924, at Tohoku University, Japan. Prof. Uda first described the antenna in *IEEJ* (Japan) in 1926. His colleague, Yagi, published the work in English, in the June 1928 *IRE Proceedings*. Thus the Yagi-Uda array is commonly called the *Yagi*. (From the IEEE history site on the internet.) I've repeated Figure 2-2 above for reference: it shows the layout of a four-element Yagi-Uda array.

Here's the yagi's anatomy. Begin with a half-wave dipole, a stack of segments which we've just studied in some detail. It will be the driven element. Attach feedline to it. Build a second dipole and place it very close, and parallel, to the first. This willl be the reflector element. It develops current by parasitic induction. To understand why, look at the driven dipole at the point in time when all the electrons are pushed to one side. They repel the electrons in the other dipole, so its current goes the other way: the two are 180° out of phase, and their radiations nearly cancel.

How the Reflector Works

Radiation from the driven element reaches the reflector 72° late for the spacing I chose. The upper phasor diagram in Figure 9-1 shows its reference phasor, D, at the reflector. The latter's current should be 180° out of phase, or 108°. But it is a bit too long. Calculations set its relative phase at 153° and amplitude at 0.77: its phasor is marked as R in the figure. The vector sum of the two, using the parallelogram rule, is shown as phasor S. This is the situation in the backward direction.

In the forward direction, shown at the bottom of the figure, the driven element phasor defines reference phase. The reflector phase is delayed by the spacing, 72°, to 81° at the driven element. Again phasors D, R, and S depict the situation.

The very bottom of the figure shows the relative size of the backward and forward total phasors. The backward one is a bit over half the length of the forward, indicating an *E* field half as strong in the rear direction, or nearly 6 dB less. This is called the *front to back* ratio. Calculations are shown below.

Put the parasitic dipole about 0.2 wavelengths - 72 electrical degrees - away from, and yet parallel to, the driven dipole. Because it takes a bit of time for the field of the driven element to reach the parasite, the latter's current is delayed somewhat. The table to the right shows NEC's calculations. Each dipole is broken into eleven segments. The first "wire" is the driven element, and current on its middle section is forced to be one ampere at reference phase.

NEC-4 calculates currents on the "wires" as shown. Not only is the parasite's current late by 180° as expected, the 72° spacing causes it to be later still. As a result, it is approximately 207° late (153° early), at the dipole's center. It thus radiates early. Its radiation is delayed by the 72° spacing before it reaches the driven element. So it reaches the driven element 81° early, and thus helps reinforce the radiation *from* the parasite *toward* the driven element. Hence the parasite is called a *reflector*.

Wire # 1	Current	
Segm3nt	Magnitude (A.)	Phase (Deg.)
1	0.18	-3.18
2	0.47	-2.77
3	0.70	-2.29
4	0.87	-1.69
5	0.97	-0.88
6	1.00	0.00
7	0.97	-0.88
8	0.87	-1.69
9	0.70	-2.29
10	0.47	-2.77
11	0.18	-3.18
Wire # 2	Current	
Segm	Magnitude (A.)	Phase (Deg.)
1	0.13	152.75
2	0.35	152.85
3	0.52	152.93
4	0.65	153.00
5	0.74	153.03
6	0.77	153.05
7	0.74	153.03
8	0.65	153.00
9	0.52	152.93
10	0.35	152.85
11	0.13	152.75

TABLE 9-1

Figure 9-2 is NEC's calculated pattern for my two element, primitive yagi. It shows that:

- The parasitic dipole acts as a reflector
- The antenna has 6.71 dBi gain, or 4.55 dB over one dipole.

Directors, when used, operate in much the same way, but have different phase shifts. They enhance radiation in the forward direction.

43

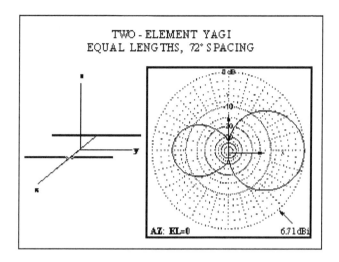

PRIMITIVE TWO ELEMENT YAGI
FIGURE 9-2

This pattern has a back lobe only about 5 dB below the gain of the forward lobe. This is the antenna's *front-to-back* ratio.

A bit of playing with the dimensions in NEC shows that a slight gain reduction, to 6.22 dBi, and a front-to-back ratio of 10.9 dB results if the reflector is lengthened to 181.4 degrees, with a driven element 172.8 degrees long, and a spacing of 50.4 degrees, *if* the elements are made of perfectly conducting, "unobtanium" [12] metal. The gain is a bit less if made of aluminum or copper.

If the reflector is instead *shortened* to 162 degrees in length, the pattern reverses, and the maximum is along the negative x axis, with a gain of 5.98 dBi and a front-to-back ratio of 8.87 dBi, using the same 72 degree element spacing. In this case the parasitic element is directing the beam from the driven element toward its direction, and is called a *director*. Notice that the better gain and front-to-back ratio is had with a single element as a reflector.

Using the single parasite as a:

- reflector   yields 6.22 dBi gain and a   10.9 dB front-to-back ratio.
- director   yields 5.98 dBi gain and an   8.87 dB front-to-back ratio.

---

[12] I was first introduced to this material by two colleagues, Drs. W. McDonald and M. Wirtz, some fifteen or so years ago.

Thus, two-element yagis with a single director can be made to work, but a single reflector works better, by a small margin. In my half-century experience, I have yet to encounter a yagi design with directors but no reflector. Yet one should be possible.

Yagis can be given many additional directors. The energy is being launched in that direction, and there is thus sufficient power to excite currents on all the directors. Designs with 16, 24, and more directors have been built. But the single reflector tends to cancel radiation moving in the reverse, driven element-to-reflector, direction. Addition of more reflectors is not very useful, for the extra reflectors have little energy available to develop much current, and thus do not do much good.

The final example of a yagi that I discuss is an example in one of the NEC software packages, [13] a five-element model. The NEC pattern is Figure 9-3, with 9.84 dBi gain. Though I do not show the pattern here, this same antenna mounted to be parallel to, and a half-wavelength above, the ground, produces a maximum gain of 13.0 dBi at an elevation angle of 25°. These values are for average ground, with $\varepsilon = 10$ and $\sigma = 10$ mS/m, at 14 MHz.

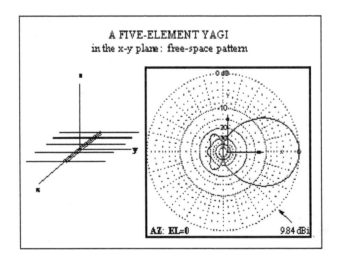

FIVE ELEMENT YAGI IN FREE SPACE
FIGURE 9-3

---

[13] EZNEC3, by Roy Lewallen, W7EL. Available at this writing via the internet. GOOGLE W7EL.

QUAD LOOP
AND THE CUBICAL QUAD

A full wavelength of wire bent into a square loop, and cut at any place for attachment of a feedline, is called a *quad loop*, as in Figure 10-1 below.

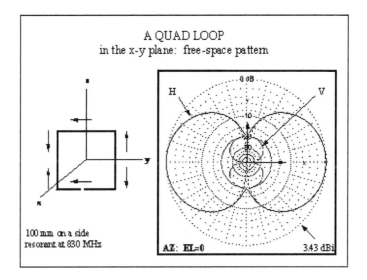

A QUAD LOOP
FIGURE 10-1

How does a designer apply the *properties of wires* in Chapter 6 to such an antenna? One would think that, beginning at the feed point and traveling around the one wavelength loop, the current ought to be maximum a quarter wave from the end, or a quarter wave from the opposite feed point. But this does not happen! The far end of the wire is not an open end, but is connected to the other side of the feed point. So the current at the far end, or at the opposite feed point terminal, need not be zero: electrons have a place to go. The current there is actually at a maximum.

At the instant when the current flows to the left in the bottom section, it continues half way up the left side, a quarter-wave from the feed point. At this point the current becomes minimum and reverses, so flows down from the top. The current drops to a minimum in the middle of the left vertical section.

The same happens in the right part of the antenna, but current flows in the opposite direction. Then it flows to the left again in the top section, in phase with the bottom. The current pattern and NEC-calculated radiation pattern are both annotated on Figure 10-1.

Given the current pattern, how can we reason out what the radiation pattern should be? First, place the camera far out the x axis. Looking back at the antenna, we see a string of segments in the top section, and in the bottom section, all horizontal and equidistant from the camera. All these segments' currents are essentially in phase. Therefore, their current moments add up and produce a strong horizontally polarized *E* field.

The left vertical section, though, is a stack of segments whose currents moments cancel. The bottom half's moments are all in phase, pointed "up," but the top half's moments all point "down." For every moment on the top, there is a corresponding moment on the bottom pointing in the opposite direction. Therefore the left half produces only vertically polarized *E* field *of zero strength*! The same argument applies to the right half of the loop.

<u>Therefore</u>:

- The radiation from the loop is horizontally polarized when fed in the middle of its bottom, as shown.
- The loop is NOT circularly polarized, as is sometimes believed!
- The loop produces a maximum along the positive and negative x axis.

Now what about along the y axis? Can you deduce that there is no radiation in this direction? Look at the right side of the loop. Again, the stack of vertical current moments, oppositely directed and otherwise in phase, cancel each other. The left half does the same. All the moments of the top and bottom horizontal sections are seen end-on. Thus there is a null along the y axis. Figure 10-1 shows a relatively deep null, 18 dB below maximum, in this direction.

Why is this null not complete? The answer is again simple. Review the discussion of the *half square* pattern, beneath Figure 6-4. The current, on its way about the quad loop, radiates energy. The current in the top half of the antenna is a bit less than that in the bottom half.

Hence the two vertical sides do *not quite* cancel their radiation, and contribute some *vertically* polarized field along the y axis. The two horizontal parts, the top and bottom, are seen end-on, so produce no horizontal field along the y axis. See Figure 10-1's heavy dotted line, the vertical field, and its lightly dotted line, the horizontal field. Clearly some vertical field shows up along the y axis.

What happens along the z axis? Looking down from the top of the antenna, the camera sees the two vertical legs as stacks of moments seen end-on. These contribute no field at all. The top horizontal part is a line of moments all pointed in one direction. It looks very much like the center half of a half-wave dipole. The radiation from these moments all add in phase, so a "horizontally" polarized signal radiates in this direction.

The bottom half also radiates as if it were the center of a half-wave dipole, and its currents are in phase with the top half. But it is a quarter wavelength farther away. Therefore, its radiation is 90° late, compared to the radiation from the top half. The total signal is only 0.7 times the maximum radiation along the x axis, or 3 dB down from maximum. (See explanation above Figure 5-8).

The Cubical Quad

Now place a second square loop along the x axis, behind the first.

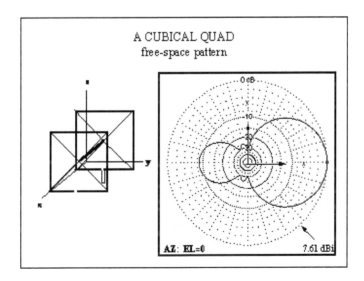

THE CUBICAL QUAD
FIGURE 10-2

With a spacing of 0.25 wavelengths, the points of the first and second loops are on the eight points of a perfect cube. Hence the "cubical" notation. But more typical spacing is about 0.2 wavelengths. Figure 10-2 shows this antenna, indicating both insulating spreaders holding the eight points of the two squares, and a central boom. The latter can be either insulating or conducting. An aluminum boom is often used.

The front loop is fed at the middle of its bottom, as before. The rear loop has a short piece of transmission line attached at its feed point, and the end of the line is shorted, as shown. This places a bit of inductance in series with its feed point, or equivalently, slightly lengthens the loop, causing the electrons to travel a bit farther. This inductive loading produces a concomitant phase shift, with a result that the front loop radiates much like a pair of dipoles, one above the other, and the rear loop does the same. The equivalent pair of dipoles on the top of the loops behaves a bit like a two-element yagi. The pair on the bottom of both loops does the same: the cubical quad acts as two yagis, ends folded down, stacked vertically a quarter wavelength apart. [14]

Optimized stacked yagis are separated a half wavelength, to null the radiation along the z axis. As an approximation to the stacked yagis, the cubical quad spacing is too close. It lets too much energy out the top and bottom. I've considered this situation and done a bit of modeling with NEC. Predictions are that stretching the loop into a rectangular shape can possibly squeeze out an additional dB or so of gain from it.

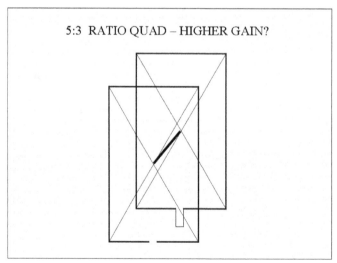

POSSIBLE HIGHER GAIN QUAD
FIGURE 10-3

---

[14] This is not an optimum spacing, as radiation leaves along the z axis. I've explored modified quads that tend to correct this problem, and achieve a gain increase of a dB or two.

Figure 10-3 is worth investigating, but I have not had time to do so yet.

Quads have a bit of a problem: made of heavy material, they tend to ice up and/or blow down in winter storms. Made of lighter, willowy material, they tend to bend about and break apart. As an investigation I designed and built a modified version of this antenna: see Figure 10-4.

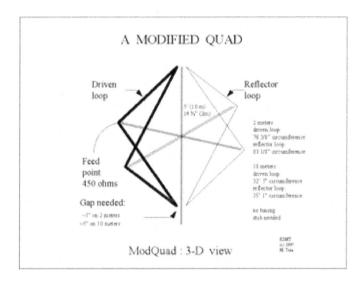

CANDIDATE FOR A SURVIVABLE QUAD
FIGURE 10-4

I built a ten meter version on a bamboo framework, the bamboo cut from a stand in my yard. Two horizontal spreaders attached to a vertical pole, and the pole itself, provided six attachment points: top and bottom of the pole and ends of the spreaders.

The "driven" loop is stretched from top of the pole, to the end of a spreader, to the bottom of the pole, and to the end of the other spreader – **not** to the end of the same spreader! The parasitic loop is similarly spread as shown in the figure.

The feedpoint was on one end of a horizontal spreader, and the stub (not shown) is attached to the parasitic loop at one of the spreaders. Thus this antenna is *vertically* polarized (use your knowledge gained so far to work out why!)

Not shown on the figure, an insulating rope "girdle" attached to the ends of the spreaders in a horizontal square loop added additional mechanical support.

I thought this *Rube Goldberg* mess would collapse before I could complete measurements. Instead, it lasted about five years, was used in weekly ten meter nets, and I finally tore it down to make room for some house repairs. The design was published on an internet web page, and lo! Permission was requested, granted, and I later saw the write-up on a club internet site in, I believe, Norwegian - I couldn't understand the language but saw my copyrighted drawings on the site!

Offered for what use you may find for this antenna –

==

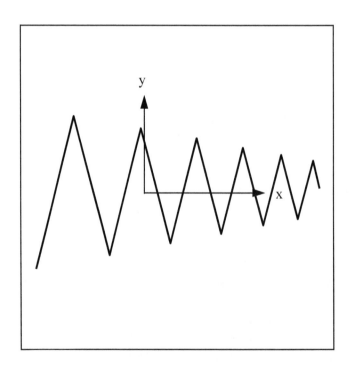

ZIG-ZAG LOG PERIODIC STRUCTURE
FIGURE 2-5

11

SIMPLE FRACTALS

A fractal antenna is one whose conductors are bent according to a repetitive mathematical relationship called a *fractal*. There are many, many fractals, and I discuss only three types here. My fractals begin with simple straight lines, and modify them according to some *motif*. The motif produces more straight lines. It can be applied again to each of these lines, to form a *second order* fractal. It may be applied again and again, to produce third, fourth, and higher order fractals.

I've already described one such device in chapter 2, and have repeated its Figure 2-5 for ready reference. In fact, it can be said that the log periodic antenna itself is a fractal.

The Fractal Quad [15]

Another example is a fractalization of Figure 10-1's square quad loop's four straight sides, as in Figure 11-1 below.

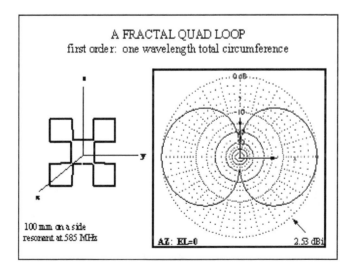

FIRST-ORDER FRACTAL QUAD LOOP
FIGURE 11-1

---

[15] An invention of Professor Nathan Cohen, Boston University.

The motif is as follows. Begin at the end of any side. Divide the side into three equal parts. Remove the center part. Then add three lines the same length as the missing center part, with a right turn, left turn, left turn, and right turn when proceeding clockwise around the loop. At obvious points where wires seem to touch, they are separated by bending them slightly out of the planar structure. Figure 11-1 shows the result, a first-order fractal loop. As in the original loop, the feed point is in the center of the bottom section.

This loop, 100 mm on a side, is resonant at 585 MHz. The loop in an unfractalized quad, Figure 10-1, again 100 mm on a side, is resonant at 830 MHz. Thus, to restore the original operating frequency, the first-order fractalized loop can be reduced in size by the ratio 585/830, or to 70 1/2% of its original size. This is one advantage of fractalizing.

Apply the motif again, to make a second-order fractal loop. Cut each straight wire into three, and apply the motif. Figure 11-2 is the result. All segments and wires fall on the y-z plane. The resonant frequency of this loop has again dropped, but not by much. It is now at 570 MHz, allowing the loop to be reduced in size just a bit more.

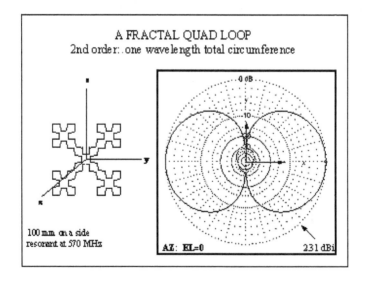

SECOND ORDER FRACTAL QUAD LOOP
FIGURE 11-2

As the loop is fractalized, notice that its calculated maximum gain drops from an initial 3.43 dBi, to 2.53 dBi, and then to 2.31 dBi. While fractalization allows a smaller loop to be used, there is some sacrifice in maximum gain, a bit over one dB.

A Zig-Zag Structure

As my second example of fractal antennas, I look a bit more closely at the structure shown in Figure 2-5, the Zig-Zag Log Periodic. It's a fine example of a fractal antenna. The wire starts at a single point along the positive x axis, and follows this motif (repeated from chapter 2):

- Stretch the wire two units out the y axis, and one unit negative along the x axis.
- Return the wire to the x axis by stretching it two units along the negative y axis, and another unit along the negative x axis.
- Choose a scaling factor, k. For example, k=0.1.
- Add 10%, to the unit size (1+k) and repeat the process as follows.
- Reverse the + and - y axis directions.
- Repeat the motif several times.

Ten and a half repetitions produces the structure of Figure 2-5. But where is its feed point?

The figure shows only one-half of a complete antenna. This *curtain* (assembly of wires, in one plane) needs another to work against, or needs some other type of counterpoise. To build a complete antenna, we need a second curtain, such as shown in plan view below, Figure 11-3.

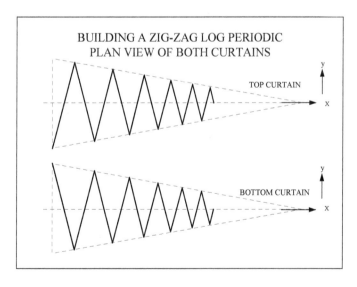

TWO ZIG-ZAG CURTAINS
FIGURE 11-3

Characteristic of log periodic antennas, these curtains fit inside an isosceles triangle, a result of the constant scaling factor, part of the motif used to build up each curtain. Notice, however, that the bottom curtain has been flipped upside down, compared to the top. This will develop a 180° phase reversal when feeding the two.

Stack the two curtains one atop the other, with the planes of their triangles making a 10° angle with the x-y plane, as shown in the side view, as below, Figure 11-4.

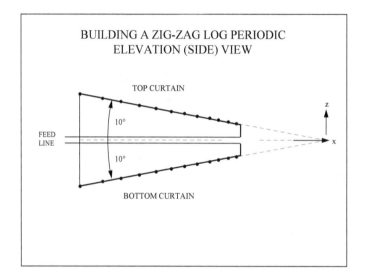

FIGURE 11-4
TWO-CURTAIN LOG PERIODIC, SIDE VIEW

Now the feed point becomes clear. The smaller ends of the curtains are connected together with a jumper, and the feedline is attached at its midpoint. The feedline is usually led out the back side of the antenna, down along a supporting boom, as shown in this view. An attempt at a 3-D view is shown in Figure 11-5. The azimuth (x-y plane) pattern of the antenna is also shown in this figure. The calculated gain of this antenna is as shown, 7.42 dBi.

The interesting property of log periodic antennas is that the pattern and gain exist at a low frequency, where the longest wire is slightly over a quarter-wave long, measured boom to tip. It continues to exist at all frequencies up to a high frequency, where the *shortest* wire is slightly *less* than a quarter-wave, again measured boom to tip. Additionally, the input impedance remains relatively constant over the same frequency range.

55

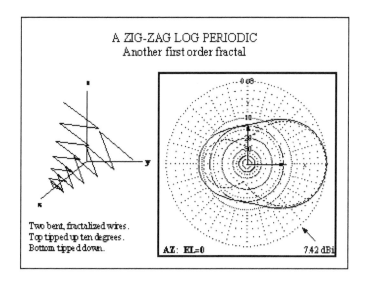

TWO-CURTAIN LOG PERIODIC -AND ITS PATTERN
FIGURE 11-5

These parameters vary in a geometric progression of frequency, such as f_1, $(1+k)f_1$, $(1+k)^2f_1$, etc, up to $(1+k)^Nf_1$, where N is about equal to the number of straight wires minus three, and k is the motif scaling factor.

In this design, N = 8.5, and k = 0.1, so the frequency range is from f_1 to $(1.10)^{8.5} f_1$. Using a simple calculator, this is a range of 2.25:1. There's nothing special about my choice of motif, only that it is one easy to explain. I've done nothing to optimize the design, and still get a useful antenna.

A Log-Periodic Sequence of Dipoles

Another interesting fractal motif begins with a half-wave, center-fed dipole. The motif scales this by some factor, and spaces it from the first dipole by another scaling factor, to form a type of 2-element yagi. But both elements are fed from one transmission line, with the line phase reversed as the new element is added. This motif is continued as often as desired.

Another way to look at this antenna is to build one curtain of a two-curtain log periodic antenna, as I do in the example, next page. Bend a wire into an L shape, one meter high and 20 cm along the bottom. Lay this wire in the x-y plane with the short part along the x axis, pointing in the positive x direction. Its long end points along the positive y direction.

Make another similarly bent, L-shaped wire, and scale it to 120% of the first wire's size. Lay its short end on the x axis, touching the long/short junction of the previous wire. Lay its long end along the *negative* y direction. Repeat this motif two more times to make the four-element curtain shown in Figure 11-6.

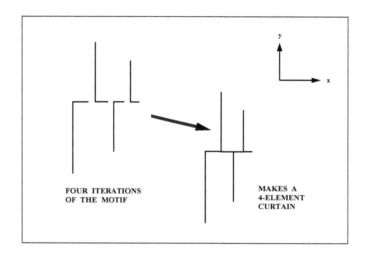

BUILDING A CURTAIN OF A STANDARD LOG PERIODIC
FIGURE 11-6

Continue the motif to make a 13-element curtain. Duplicate this curtain, and turn it upside-down, as in Figure 11-7.

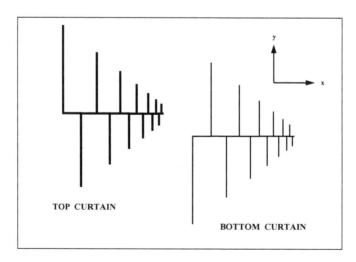

MAKING TWO CURTAINS OF A LOG PERIODIC
FIGURE 11-7

57

Finally, place one curtain beneath the other, as in Figure 11-8. The series of short sections of the L shaped wires form a boom for each curtain, and these two booms are separated a bit, one above the other, to form a transmission line. The feedline from the transmitter or receiver is attached to the transmission line at the short end, at the right side in these figures.

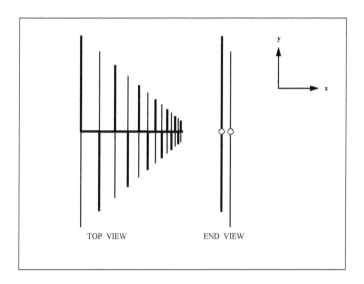

MAKING THE TOTAL ANTENNA FROM TWO CURTAINS
FIGURE 11-8

The shortest dipole of this antenna is 2 m, end to end, and would resonate at about 70 MHz in free space. As a director in a yagi antenna, it would resonate at a slightly lesser frequency. The longest dipole is 17.8 m end-to-end [16] and would resonate in free space at 8.5 MHz. It would serve as a yagi *reflector* near 10 MHz.

In Figure 11-9, currents on the antenna are shown as bowed, dotted lines. This is a type of graph, the distance between the line proportional to the current. The figure is from the ARRL antenna book, a fine general reference on log periodics and antennas in general, intended for the amateur radio audience.

Driving this antenna at 10 MHz produces currents on the longest three elements, and much less on the other elements, as shown in the left half of Figure 11-9.

---

[16] Scaling factor, 1.2, raised to the 12th power, times the length of the shortest dipole.

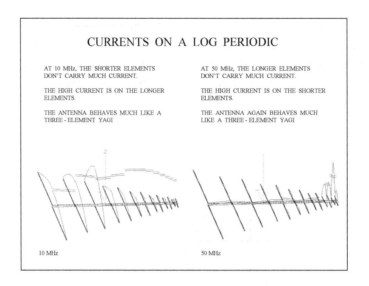

CURRENT DISTRIBUTION VARYING WITH FREQUENCY
From the ARRL Antenna Book
FIGURE 11-9

Driving it at 50 MHz, on the other hand, produces current on the shortest three elements, and much less on the others, as seen in the right half of the figure. This log periodic, then, behaves somewhat as a sequence of three-element yagis, with the maximum current occurring along the antenna as a function of frequency, from the left end to the right end, as frequency increases.

The pairs of dashed lines above the structure in the left side of the figure are the currents flowing on the two wires of the transmission line. This suggests that the antenna should perform over an extended frequency range, dictated by the ratio of longest element to shortest element lengths. Indeed, Figure 11-10 shows the behavior of the antenna's SWR as frequency changes, and Figure 11-11 shows the radiation pattern in the x-y plane for four spot frequencies between 10 and 50 MHz.

The log periodic is an example of a fractal antenna of but a single order of fractalization. That is, the motif is applied only once. In general, fractal antennas have been studies with 2nd, 3rd, 4th, and higher orders of fractalization.

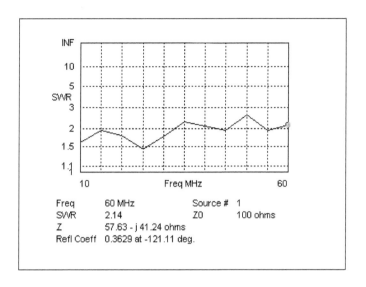

LOG PERIODIC SWR - 100 OHM LINE
From the ARRL Antenna Book
FIGURE 11-10

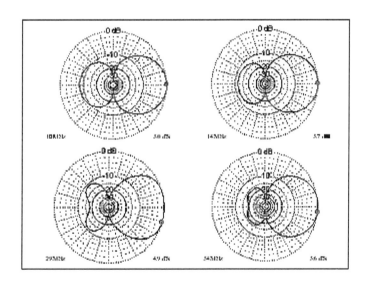

AZIMUTH PATTERNS AT FOUR FREQUENCIES
From the ARRL Antenna Book
FIGURE 11-11

NOTES

12

DIPOLE CURTAINS
AND CURRENT TAPERING

The Double Dipole

A single dipole has a gain of 2.15 dBi and an overall length a bit less than a half-wavelength. Placing two in a line, end-to-end, as in Figure 12-1, doubles the field strength along a line perpendicular to the dipoles, provided the two carry exactly the same current, in magnitude and phase. The doubling of field strength suggests a 6 dB gain over one dipole. But it takes twice as much power to drive two dipoles, thus requiring 3 dB more power. So the net gain is 3 dB.

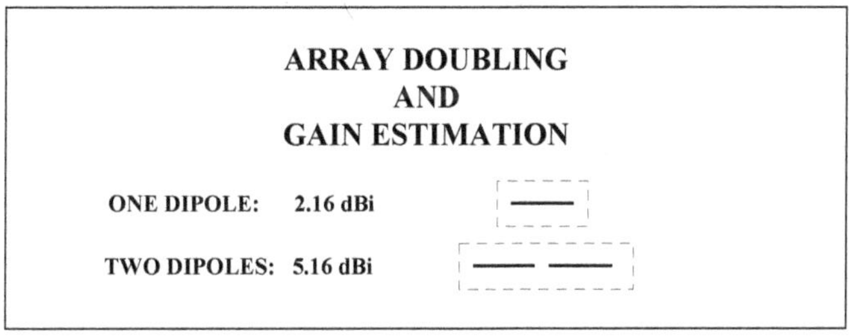

ARRAY DOUBLING
AND
GAIN ESTIMATION

ONE DIPOLE: 2.16 dBi

TWO DIPOLES: 5.16 dBi

GAIN BOOST FROM DOUBLING AN ANTENNA'S SIZE
FIGURE 12-1

This is a general rule of thumb: making a new antenna by combining two smaller ones, or doubling the size of an antenna array, doubles the gain.

Four and Eight Dipole Arrays

Doubling the size of the two-dipole array can be done by making a second, identical array and placing it above the first, spaced again one-half wavelength from the bottom dipoles. The antenna can be again doubled in size by making a second four-dipole array and placing it alongside the first one. Now we develop an array of two lines of dipoles, four on a line.

The inter-dipole spacing along a line is one-half wavelength, [17] and the two lines are spaced a half-wavelength. Figure 12-2 depicts the two additional doublings of the two-dipole array to an array of eight dipoles.

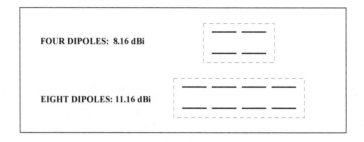

FOUR DIPOLES: 8.16 dBi

EIGHT DIPOLES: 11.16 dBi

TWO DOUBLINGS OF THE ARRAY
FIGURE 12-2

Four By Four, Sixteen-Dipole Array

Finally, another doubling is done by making a duplicate of the eight-dipole array and stacking it atop the first, to make the 4 by 4 dipole array shown in Figure 12-3.

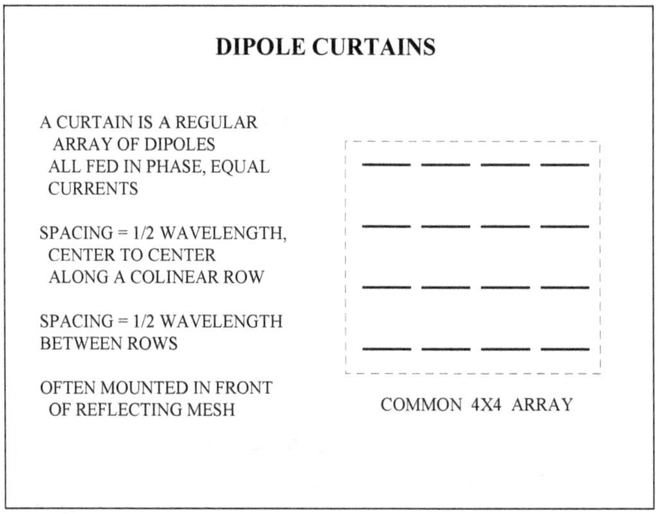

DIPOLE CURTAINS

A CURTAIN IS A REGULAR
ARRAY OF DIPOLES
ALL FED IN PHASE, EQUAL
CURRENTS

SPACING = 1/2 WAVELENGTH,
CENTER TO CENTER
ALONG A COLINEAR ROW

SPACING = 1/2 WAVELENGTH
BETWEEN ROWS

OFTEN MOUNTED IN FRONT
OF REFLECTING MESH

COMMON 4X4 ARRAY

THE COMMON 4 X 4 SHORTWAVE ANTENNA
FIGURE 12-3

---

[17] So why don't their ends touch each other? The resonant length of a dipole is just a bit less than a half wave, so there is a short interdipole gap along a line.

The additional doubling adds 3 dB more gain to the array, and mounting it in front of a reflecting grid of wires (not shown) generates an image of the 16 dipoles, raising the estimated gain of this antenna to 17.24 dBi.

Notice that this array has 16 dipoles, all carrying the same current (in magnitude and phase), and the dipoles are spaced a half-wavelength, both horizontally and vertically. There is a trick, of course, to driving all currents to be the same, but I do not go into that here. It is done commercially.

A version of this 16-dipole, 4 x 4 array, was used in very early WW II radars, and a similar antenna was used at the Diana radar site of Fort Monmouth, NJ, in the first Earth-Moon-Earth - Moonbounce - demonstration.

Figure 12-4 shows the calculated pattern of this antenna. In the computer program, the x-y plane can easily be made to form a reflecting surface, so the coordinates in this figure have the antenna parallel to the x-y plane, and the beam formed, shown as straight overhead, is actually directed at right angles to the face of the array, i.e., directly out of the paper at you.

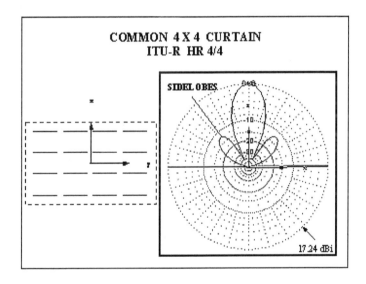

PATTERN OF THE 4 X 4 CURTAIN
FIGURE 12-4

This antenna is one of a standard set, listed by the International Telecommunications Union Radio division, designated as the ITU HR 4/4 antenna.

H means it is horizontally polarized, R that it has a reflecting screen, and 4 / 4 refers to the number of dipoles arrayed horizontally and vertically, respectively.

Current Tapering and Sidelobe Reduction

The pattern of Figure 12-4 shows the existence of two sidelobes about 12 dB down from the main lobe. There are times when such sidelobes can be troublesome. One is when a terrestrial station transmits to a geosynchronous satellite: sidelobes can put undesired energy into the antenna of an adjacent satellite. How can these lobes be reduced?

In Figure 12-5 I show the buildup of an array with other than identical currents on all elements.

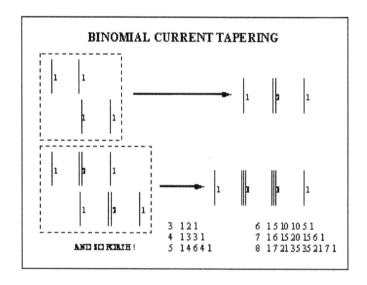

CURRENT TAPERING
FIGURE 12-5

At the upper left. build an array by starting with two dipoles carrying identical currents, one ampere each. I've made a copy of this array directly below the original, with its center spaced one half wavelength from the original's center. To the right I overlap these two, to form a 3-element array. The current on the outer two elements is one ampere, but the current in the center, combined element is two amperes.

64

Next, take this three-element array to the lower left. Again duplicate it, and space the two with their centers a half-wavelength apart. Then, by overlapping the two at the lower right, form an array of four dipoles. The outside two carry one ampere, but the inside two are now tripled elements, and carry three amperes.

In a similar fashion, proceed to make an array of as many elements as is desired. The currents on the elements follow the amplitude variations shown in the figure. These sequences of numbers are familiar to high school algebra students: they are the successive terms in Pascal's triangle, also called the binomial coefficients. Therefore, this variation, or *tapering*, of currents across the array is called a binomial tapering. [18]

Figure 12-6 shows the effect on the pattern of the HR 4 / 4: **no sidelobes** – but a slight gain reduction.

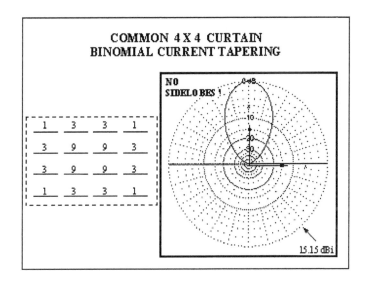

LOBE REDUCTION BY BINOMIAL TAPERING
FIGURE 12-6

The current tapering is applied across the bottom row of dipoles, in a 1 - 3 - 3 - 1 pattern, and across the top row. It is also applied down the left and right columns of dipoles. Then it is applied across the inner two rows, with a relative 1 - 3 - 3 - 1 current pattern.

---

[18] Mathematicians note: in the limit of a very large number of elements, the binomial tapering melds into a gaussian taper of currents.

65

But the outer dipoles of these rows already carry three amperes of current, so these two rows have a net 3 - 9 - 9 - 3 current profile. Finally, we find that the same current pattern results, looking down the inner two columns.

The calculated pattern of the antenna with this current tapering profile appears on the right of Figure 12-6. It differs from the previous pattern in three interesting ways:

1. The sidelobes are reduced in amplitude. In fact, with binomial current tapering, they disappear entirely!
2. The main lobe is not as sharply defined.
3. The main lobe gain is lower, having dropped a bit over 2 dB.

A General Characteristic of Current Tapering

Look more carefully at Figure 12-6. There is a central "hot spot" surrounded by a much cooler ring. The hot spot contains four dipoles, and the ring contains twelve. Thus there is a sort of perversity to current tapering. Three fourths of the antenna's total "real estate" - its area - really doesn't work very hard. But it costs money to build, nonetheless.

This concept of current tapering, or reduction of RF power from the center to the edges of a larger antenna structure, finds application in the design of large reflector antennas, such as parabolic dishes. In these reflectors, the majority of the antenna's real estate does a very minor amount of work. But the work it does is important in boosting antenna gain while keeping minor radiation lobes under control.

13

SUMMARY

Principles developed in this book can be summarized as follows.

1. Any collection of bent wires that carry radio currents is an antenna.
2. Any pile of tin is an antenna. Just attach a transmission line.
3. Antenna engineering works out how much wire or tin to use and how to bend or shape it.
4. Antennas are collections of interconnected, short wire segments.
5. Each segment is short enough that the current it carries is essentially constant.
6. The product of a segment length and its current is called a current moment.
7. The current moments create the radiated radio field.
8. There is no radiation directly off the end of a segment.
9. The total field created by an antenna is the sum of fields from all the current moments.
10. The Pattern of an antenna shows the field strength at each azimuth and elevation angle from the center of an antenna.
11. Computer programs make the calculation of currents much easier.
12. The current at the end of an unconnected wire must be zero.
13. Current at odd multiples of a quarter wavelength from an end will be a relative maximum.
14. Current at even multiples of a quarter wavelength from an end will be at a minimum.
15. Current direction reverses at current minima.
16. Doubling the size of an antenna by merging two antennas into one usually doubles the gain, an increase of 3 dB.

==

Definition of dB

The ratio of two powers can be expressed in *bels* [19] by the formula $bel = \log(P_1 / P_0)$, where P_0 is a **reference** power. It expresses the ratio of two powers. This reference level must always be unambiguously clear to the reader.

The bel is a rather large unit, so we divide it into tenths, and call these dB, or decibels. Since power is proportional to the square of voltage or current, bel ratios are 2 times the log of voltage or current ratios. dB then is given as $20 \log (V_1 / V_0)$.

Some common ratios are: -3 dB = half power   -6 dB = one-fourth power
       -10 dB = 1/10th power.   -20 dB = 1/100 th power   -30 dB = 1/1000 th power

                              +3 dB = double power   +6 dB = four times power
       +10 dB = ten times   +20 dB = hundred times   +30 dB = 1000 times

==

---

[19] The bel is named after Alexander Graham Bell. Hence, the protocol for writing the unit abbreviated is capitalized, e.g., B. When spelled out, it is given in lowercase, e.g., bel, as uppercase spelling means the honorees name. For example, volt, V; watt, W; ampere, A, ohm, Ω.

GLOSSARY

Amplitude	Strength, or magnitude.
Azimuth Pattern	A cut through the antenna pattern in the horizontal, x-y, plane.
bel	A fundamental unit of power ratios. Rarely used. Tenths are usually used as decibels, or dB.
Circular Polarization	(Not explained in the text). A situation where two radio antennas produce vertical and horizontal polarization, phased 90 degrees apart. If one is weaker than the other, they produce elliptical polarization.
Curtain	A group of antenna elements contained in one flat plane.
decibels, dB	A ratio of two powers, in logarithmic terms. $dB = 10 \log(P_1/P_0)$, where P_0 is the reference power. dB is also 20 times the log of a voltage or current ratio.
dBi	Power relative to an isotropic antenna, in dB format.
Degree	Another measure of length where 1 wavelength = 360°. A measure of timing difference between phasors.
dBuV/m	Radiated power relative to a microvolt per meter, in dB format. A fundamental unit of radio field strength.
Dipole	A straight wire antenna, cut in its middle for attachment of transmission line.
Director	An antenna element that draws the radiation pattern in its direction.
Driven element	An antenna element connected to a receiver or transmitter through a feedline.

E field	Electric field, both in strength and direction (a vector).
Electrical degree	Degree of length.
Element	A current-carrying part of an antenna.
Elevation Pattern	A cut through the antenna pattern containing the z axis.
Excite	Put RF power into an antenna.
Elmer	A person who trains another to become a radio amateur.
Feedline	Transmission line used to connect radio equipment to an antenna.
Fractal	A mathematical line, plane, or solid with a repeating structure. Also, an antenna whose elements are built on fractal motifs.
Front-to-Back ratio	The main lobe gain, minus the gain of the lobe in the rearward direction, both in dB.
Gain	Antenna pattern power output relative to some reference, customarily an isotropic antenna, there expressed in dBi.
Half Wavelength	A length equal to half of a wavelength.
Impedance	The sum of resistance and reactance.
Isotropic	A unit gain antenna, that has 0 dB radiation in all directions. Used as a reference when calculating absolute antenna power patterns.
Lobe	Direction where the antenna pattern has a locally maximum gain. The gain at nearby locations is less.
NEC	Numerical Electromagnetic Code, a method-of-moments computer program that calculates the performance of antennas.
Origin	Junction of x, y, and z axis. The center from which measurements are taken.

Magnitude	Strength of a radio signal. Synonymous with *Amplitude*.
Main Lobe	The largest lobe of an antenna pattern.
Null	Opposite of a lobe: a direction in which the antenna pattern has minimum radiation.
Parasite	An element of an antenna that has no connection to a transmission line, but develops current by induction from the other elements,
Phase	Timing of an oscillating radio signal, compared to a reference time.
Phasor	A vector showing the magnitude and relative phase of the E field from a segment, moment, or other part of an antenna.
Polarization	Direction in which the electric field points. May be vertical, horizontal, tilted, or rotate.
Radiation	Production of a radio field, an electric field, or radio power. Radio (Electromagnetic) energy.
Reactance	Similar to resistance, but the current is 90° out of step with the voltage.
Reflector	An antenna element that directs radiation away from itself, back toward the driven element.
Resistance	Opposition to current flow, where the current is always in phase with the voltage, and equal to voltage divided by current.
Resonance	A condition where the voltage driving the antenna produces current in phase with the voltage.
Segment	A very small portion of an antenna, usually less than 1/20 th of a wavelength.
Shortwave	Frequencies between 3 and 30 MHz.

Side Lobe	A lobe whose gain is less than the main lobe.
Small	Physical size of an antenna, when quite less than a quarter wavelength. At 300 MHz, less than 20 cm. At 1 MHz, less than 70 meters.
Spatial	Phase shifts caused by spacing between segments or antennas.
Temporal	Phase shifts due to time phasing of the exciting currents.
Transmission line	Coaxial cable or balanced wire.
Vector	Any quantity having both size (magnitude) and direction. Velocity is a vector. It makes a difference if you are on an interstate, doing 70 mph, Westbound vice Eastbound.
Wave	Wavelength.
Wavelength	A unit of length, in meters, equal to 300 / frequency in MHz.
x and y axes	Two lines intersecting in a right angle, that define a horizontal plane. They also intersect the z axis in a right angle.
z axis	A vertical line pointing "up."